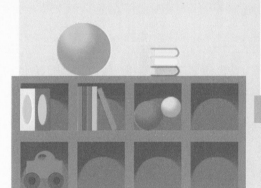

BLACK BOYS DANCE TOO
"DARNELL ENTERS A TALENT SHOW"

Written by: Jamal Josef

Illustrated by: Adrian Turner

Today is the first day of school. Darnell wakes up to put on his clothes, brushes his teeth, and runs downstairs.

With so much excitement, Darnell rushes to finish his cereal. "Slow down son and chew your food," his mother says with a laugh. "I'm finished!" Darnell shouts, and off to school he goes.

"Good morning class! My name is Mrs. Smith. Welcome to your first day of school. Let's start our day with a game. Stand and say your name, then tell us when you are in the sun what you do for fun."

Darnell stands up and says "My name is Darnell and I like to dance."
There was a moment of silence, and then he heard the class laugh.
"Hahaha! My mom says dance is for girls! Boys do not swirl and twirl!"
a classmate shouts.
"That's the silliest thing I have ever heard. In our classroom,
we use positive words. Dancing is for girls and boys," Mrs. Smith says.

After hours of learning, it's time for fun.
"Now is the time we all love: RECESS. Class, stand, push in your chairs, and line up quietly," Mrs. Smith says.

Darnell still did not understand why everyone laughed at him. Darnell thinks to himself, "I guess I can try something new."

Darnell sees a group of boys playing basketball and thinks to himself, "I guess I can try something new."

"Can I play?" Darnell asks. He dribbles, he shoots, he misses the shot. "Airballll!" the students laughed and shouted.

The next day during recess, he tries football. Oh my, more laughs. Trying to fit in was not working.

As months went by, Darnell thought he would make more friends.
"Mom, Dad, why don't I fit in?" Darnell asks.
"Well Darnell you have a gift and you must use the gifts you are given.
No matter what, we love you, and you are talented." say his parents.

The next day of school, Darnell signed up for the talent show as a dancer. He practiced every day during recess.

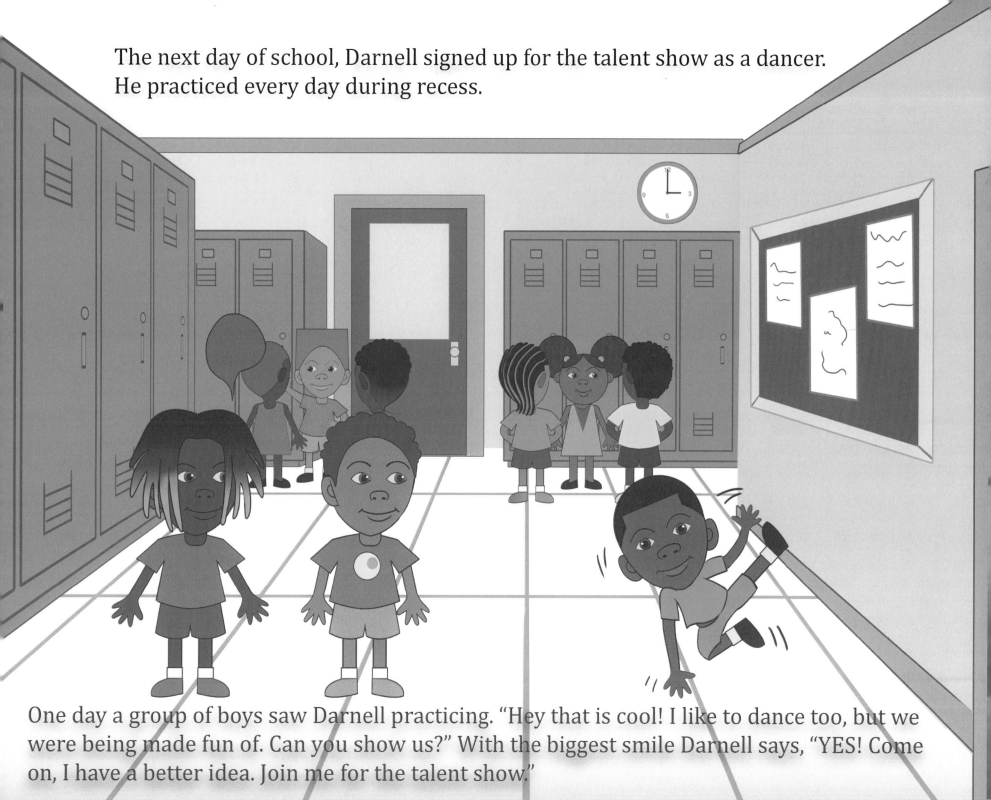

One day a group of boys saw Darnell practicing. "Hey that is cool! I like to dance too, but we were being made fun of. Can you show us?" With the biggest smile Darnell says, "YES! Come on, I have a better idea. Join me for the talent show."

The boys practiced every day until the show. "Ok class, tonight is the talent show. Come on out to cheer on your fellow classmates," says Mrs. Smith.

Ladies and Gentlemen, boys and girls welcome to the school talent show! The show begins. Darnell hears the announcements, the crowd cheering, singing, and instruments.

Finally, it was his turn. Darnell and his friends get on the stage. The music comes on. Step touch, step touch, kick, spin, turn and jump. The crowd shouts, "Darnell, Darnell, Darnell !!!" With a ROUND OF APPLAUSE...

"Now (the moment everyone has been waiting for) this year's first-place goes to, drum roll please....Darnell and his dance crew!" The crowd goes wild and as Darnell grabs the trophy, he looks over to his parents and smiles.

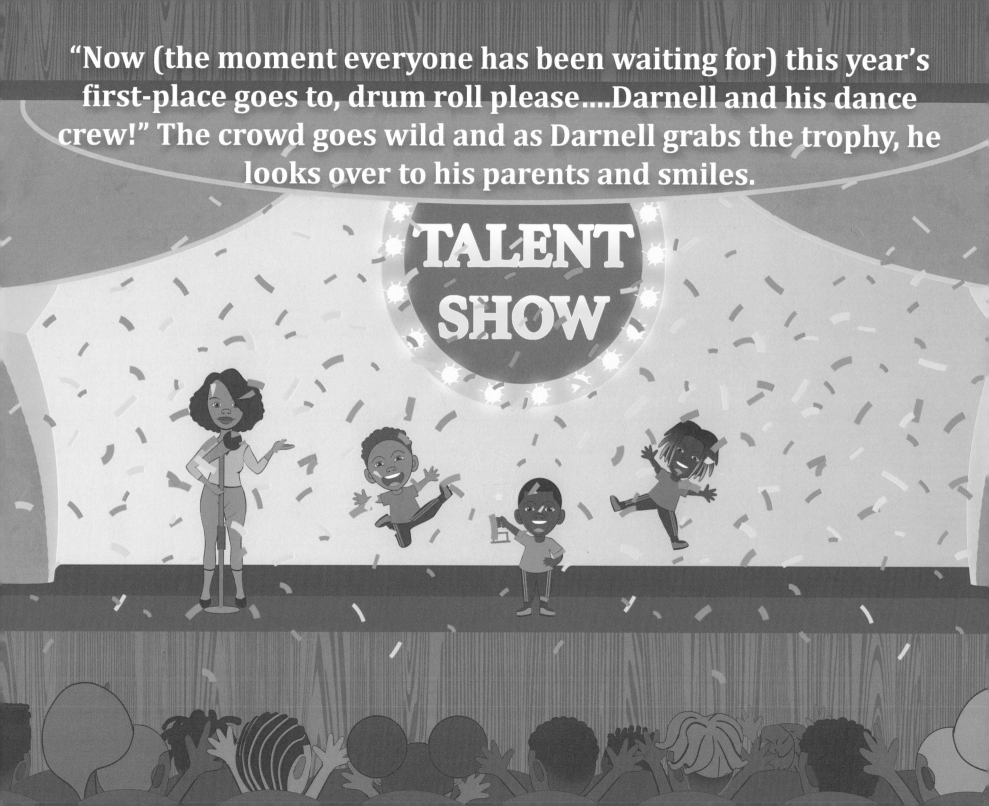

"Any words you would like to say Darnell?" Mrs. Smith asks.

Darnell grabs the mic and proudly says, "Yes WE ARE YOUNG BLACK BOYS, TALENTED, AND WE ARE DANCERS!"

CPSIA information can be obtained
at www.ICGtesting.com
Printed in the USA
LVRC101306280421
685854LV00013B/102